Guidance notes and flow charts for the

Adjudicator's Contract

This contract should be used for the appointment of an Adjudicator to decide disputes under the NEC family of contracts. It may also be used for the appointment of an Adjudicator under other forms of contract

An NEC document

June 2005

Construction Clients' Board endorsement of NEC3

The Construction Clients' Board (formerly Public Sector Construction Clients' Forum) recommends that public sector organisations use the NEC3 contracts when procuring construction. Standardising use of this comprehensive suite of contracts should help to deliver efficiencies across the public sector and promote behaviours in line with the principles of *Achieving Excellence in Construction*.

NEC is a division of Thomas Telford Ltd, which is a wholly owned subsidiary of the Institution of Civil Engineers (ICE), the owner and developer of the NEC.

The NEC is a family of standard contracts, each of which has these characteristics:

- Its use stimulates good management of the relationship between the two parties to the contract and, hence, of the work included in the contract.
- It can be used in a wide variety of commercial situations, for a wide variety of types of work and in any location.
- It is a clear and simple document – using language and a structure which are straightforward and easily understood.

This document comprises the Guidance Notes and Flow Charts for the NEC Adjudicator's Contract.

ISBN (complete box set) 978 07277 3675 8
ISBN (this document) 978 07277 3375 7
ISBN (Adjudicator's Contract) 978 07277 3374 0

First edition 1994
Second edition 1998
Third edition June 2005
Reprinted 2007, 2010, 2012

Cover photo, Golden Jubilee Bridge, courtesy of City of Westminster

9 8 7 6 5 4 3 2

British Library Cataloguing in Publication Data for this publication is available from the British Library.

Typeset by Academic + Technical, Bristol

Printed and bound in Great Britain by Bell & Bain Limited, Glasgow, UK

CONTENTS

ACKNOWLEDGEMENTS

The first edition of the NEC Adjudicator's Contract was drafted by Peter Higgins working on behalf of the Institution of Civil Engineers with the assistance of Frank Griffiths of the Chartered Institute of Purchasing and Supply and Michael Coleman of the Association of Project Managers. Dr Martin Barnes of Coopers and Lybrand advised on the co-ordination of the contract with the NEC.

For the second edition of the NEC Adjudicator's Contract the guidance notes were produced by the Institution of Civil Engineers through its NEC Panel and were mainly drafted by Bill Weddell, with the assistance of Peter Higgins and Tom Nicholson, as members of the NEC Panel. The flow charts were produced by John Perry, Ross Hayes and colleagues at the University of Birmingham.

For the third edition of the NEC Adjudicator's Contract these guidance notes were mainly drafted by Peter Higgins with the assistance of members of the NEC Panel. The Flow Charts were produced by Robert Gerrard with assistance from Ross Hayes and Tom Nicholson.

The original NEC was designed and drafted by Dr Martin Barnes then of Coopers and Lybrand with the assistance of Professor J. G. Perry then of the University of Birmingham, T. W. Weddell then of Travers Morgan Management, T. H. Nicholson, Consultant to the Institution of Civil Engineers, A. Norman then of the University of Manchester Institute of Science and Technology and P. A. Baird, then Corporate Contracts Consultant, Eskom, South Africa.

The members of the NEC Panel are:

P. Higgins, BSc, CEng, FICE, FCIArb (Chairman)
P. A. Baird, BSc, CEng, FICE, M(SA)ICE, MAPM
M. Barnes, BSc(Eng), PhD, FREng, FICE, FCIOB, CCMI, ACIArb, MBCS, FInstCES, FAPM
A. J. Bates, FRICS, MInstCES
A. J. M. Blackler, BA, LLB(Cantab), MCIArb
P. T. Cousins, BEng(Tech), DipArb, CEng, MICE, MCIArb, MCMI
L. T. Eames, BSc, FRICS, FCIOB
F. Forward, BA(Hons), DipArch, MSc(Const Law), RIBA, FCIArb
Professor J. G. Perry, MEng, PhD, CEng, FICE, MAPM
N. C. Shaw, FCIPS, CEng, MIMechE
T. W. Weddell, BSc, CEng, DIC, FICE, FIStructE, ACIArb

NEC Consultant:

R. A. Gerrard, BSc(Hons), MRICS, FCIArb, FInstCES

Secretariat:

A. Cole, LLB, LLM, BL
J. M. Hawkins, BA(Hons), MSc
F. N. Vernon (Technical Adviser), BSc, CEng, MICE

⬤nec™3 Adjudicator's Contract Guidance Notes

INTRODUCTION

The first edition of the NEC Adjudicator's Contract, published in 1994, was written for the appointment of an adjudicator for any contract under the NEC family of standard contracts.

The second edition, published in 1998, incorporated changes and improvements which had been found necessary after experience of its use. It also incorporated changes arising from the need to harmonise with the NEC standard contracts and further editions which had been issued since 1994.

This third edition is published as part of a re-issue of all the NEC documents. Further changes have been made to harmonise the contract with the new editions of the NEC standard contracts. In particular, the contract has been written to be used with either of the adjudication Options.

Use of the Adjudicator's Contract

The adjudication clauses in NEC contracts provide for the Adjudicator being appointed under the Adjudicator's Contract. This is so whether the Adjudicator was named in the contract, was selected or replaced later, or was chosen by a nominating body. The detailed procedures for adjudication are included in the respective NEC contracts and so are not repeated in this document.

This Adjudicator's Contract may also be used for the appointment of an adjudicator under forms of contract other than those in the NEC family. If so, there may be conflict between the Adjudicator's Contract and the *contract between the Parties*, for example Expenses, payment arrangements and termination. Since subclause 1.7 gives priority to the Adjudicator's Contract for the reasons explained below, it may be necessary to amend either contract to resolve such conflict.

Scheme adjudications

In the UK, the Housing Grants, Construction and Regeneration Act 1996 has made adjudication mandatory as a means of resolving disputes in certain construction contracts. Parties to a contract which does not provide for adjudication as required by the Act have a right to adjudication under the 'Scheme for Construction Contracts' (the Scheme). Schemes which are substantially similar have been published for England and Wales, Scotland and Northern Ireland.

It is possible that the parties may wish to use this Adjudicator's Contract for appointing an adjudicator under the Scheme. If this contract is used, an additional entry should be made in the Contract Data, recording the agreement that the Adjudicator is to decide the apportionment of his *fee* and Expenses between the Parties. This replaces the fallback position of subclause 3.2 under which the Parties pay in equal shares. In the identification of the *contract between the parties*, the relevant Scheme should be identified as well as the contract documents.

Selection of Adjudicator

No procedures have been specified for appointing a suitable person, and in practice a number of different methods have been used. Whatever method is used, it is important that both Parties have full confidence in his impartiality, and for that reason it is preferable that a joint appointment is made. The Adjudicator should be a person with experience in the type of work included in the *contract between the Parties* and who occupies or has occupied a senior position dealing with disputes. He should be able to understand the viewpoint of both Parties.

Often the Parties delay selecting an adjudicator until a dispute has arisen, although this frequently results in a disagreement over who should be the Adjudicator. As noted, the selection of the Adjudicator is important, and it should be recognised that a failure to agree an adjudicator means that a third party will make the selection without necessarily consulting the Parties.

The purpose of these guidance notes is to explain the reasons for the provisions in the Adjudicator's Contract and to provide guidance on how to use it. The flow charts are for reference in conjunction with the guidance notes. Neither the guidance notes nor the flow charts are part of the Adjudicator's Contract and should not be used for legal interpretation of its meaning.

FORM OF AGREEMENT

This contract uses a Form of Agreement as a convenient means for the two Parties and the Adjudicator to record their agreement to the appointment of the Adjudicator. It is drafted as a simple contract.

An Adjudicator may be either named in the contract between the Parties, or may be nominated or selected later.

Where the contract requires an Adjudicator to be named in the contract, the Form of Agreement should be completed and signed by both Parties and the Adjudicator as soon as possible after the *contract between the Parties* comes into being.

Where the contract requires an Adjudicator to be appointed only after a dispute has arisen, as in many other forms of contract, the Form of Agreement should be completed and signed by the Parties and the selected or nominated Adjudicator immediately after selection or nomination.

CONDITIONS OF CONTRACT

1 General

Actions 1.1   This subclause states the general obligations of the Parties and the Adjudicator in terms of two contracts; the Adjudicator's Contract and the *contract between the Parties*. In the event that there is conflict between these two contracts, the former has priority as stated in subclause 1.7. Where the Scheme applies, the various obligations outlined in the Scheme are also included by identifying the Scheme procedures as a contract requirement.

The requirement for the Adjudicator to act impartially is fundamental to the whole system of adjudication. Any failure by the Adjudicator to so act would be a serious breach of his obligations.

The *contract between the Parties* may include procedures and timing requirements to be followed by the Parties and the Adjudicator in the adjudication process. Such procedures are included in the adjudication clauses of the NEC contracts. These procedures and requirements are incorporated by reference into this Adjudicator's Contract. The procedures and requirements in the Scheme are similarly incorporated when it has been agreed by the Parties or imposed by statute.

The duties and procedures to be followed are stated in the present tense for simplicity, as in other NEC documents. Where actions are permitted but not obligatory, the term 'may' is used.

1.2   The purpose of this subclause is to identify any matter which may affect the Adjudicator in carrying out his duties. The consequences of the notification are not stated since they will vary according to the circumstances.

For instance, a contractor may enter into a subcontract with a subcontractor with whom the Adjudicator may have some connection. The Parties on being so informed may decide that the conflict of interest is so small that they are content for the Adjudicator to continue and to rely on his duty to act impartially. Alternatively, they may decide to terminate his appointment under the termination clause.

Identified and defined terms   1.3   The conventions described are those generally followed throughout the NEC contracts. The Adjudicator and the Parties are those named in the Form of Agreement. For clarity, the same conventions of italics and capital initials are used in these guidance notes.

Interpretation   1.7   The *contract between the Parties* may conflict with provisions in the Adjudicator's Contract. This subclause establishes priorities where there is such conflict. Priority has been given to the Adjudicator's Contract as the Adjudicator will not normally have been provided with a copy of the entire *contract between the Parties* when he is appointed. Where an adjudication takes place under the Scheme, imposed by operation of statute, the Scheme will automatically have priority over the Adjudicator's Contract and the *contract between the Parties*.

   1.8   If the *contract between the Parties* has a 'joinder' clause, it may be that a dispute in a subcontract may also comprise a dispute in the main contract. The 'joinder' provisions permit the subcontractor to be joined as a party involved in the dispute in the main contract adjudication. Thus, the Adjudicator's Contract is interpreted such that the term 'Parties' includes the subcontractor.

Communications   1.9   The phrase 'in a form which can be read, copied and recorded' includes a letter sent by post, telex, cable, electronic mail, facsimile transmission, and on disc, magnetic tape or other electronic means.

   1.10   Communications are effective only when they have been received. This means that the date for making a decision and notifying the Parties of it runs from the date of receipt, not of posting the referral. Note, however, that the Scheme provides for communications being effective when posted. If the Scheme has been imposed on the contract by statute, that will take precedence over this subclause.

2 Adjudication

   2.1   Once a dispute has been adjudicated on, the decision can either be accepted or referred to the tribunal named in the *contract between the Parties*. It cannot be subject to adjudication again, even if a new Adjudicator has been appointed.

   2.2   It is important that the Adjudicator clearly identifies the issue which is in dispute and then gives a decision only on that dispute. In everything he does he must follow any procedures laid down in the *contract between the Parties* and in the Scheme where applicable. It follows that the Adjudicator should be aware of all the relevant provisions in the *contract between the Parties* and in any relevant Scheme. Any departure from these may give a Party grounds for challenging his decision. No timing is stated in this subclause. If the *contract between the Parties* does not include timing for an adjudication, and if there are no relevant statutory requirements, the Parties and the Adjudicator should seek to agree appropriate times in order to avoid delay. Under the NEC contracts the Adjudicator is required also to give reasons for his decisions.

   2.3   This subclause gives the Adjudicator a power in addition to those he may have in the *contract between the Parties*. The purpose in giving the Adjudicator this power is to enable him to arrive at a fair settlement of the dispute within the time available. However, any decision he makes must be his own. Any payments he makes to specialists under this subclause are part of Expenses as defined in subclause 1.4.

The Adjudicator must inform the Parties that he is seeking help from others, and he must allow the Parties the opportunity of commenting on the advice he has received. The Scheme includes a similar power to 'appoint experts, assessors or legal advisers', provided that the Adjudicator notifies the Parties of his intention.

2.5   It is possible that the Adjudicator's decision can be used to resolve other disputes between the Parties which have not been notified. This subclause limits the further use which the Parties may make of the Adjudicator's decision. However, there may be many who need to be advised of the Adjudicator's decision. These may include a Party's bank or insurer, an auditor or a parent company. These are quite legitimate and permissible.

3 Payment

Advanced payment   3.1   The timescale for adjudication does not lend itself to either interim payments or holding on to the decision until payment is made. This subclause permits the use of advanced payments to secure the Adjudicator's *fee*. The level of advance set should recognise the level of work likely to be needed for a dispute; a larger advanced payment would be appropriate for a more substantial project as the disputes will potentially be more complex. If no advanced payment is to be made, 'Nil' should be entered in the Contract Data. If an advanced payment is made, credit for that payment is given in the Adjudicator's assessment of the amount due.

Advanced payment is made by the party referring the dispute. This avoids the possibility of a 'strategic' delay by the other Party refusing to pay a share. In the final decision and invoice, the Adjudicator should take into account the Parties' relative obligations to pay his fees and adjust the amounts accordingly. For example, if the Parties are each liable for equal shares, in a decision the Adjudicator will require the other Party to pay half the advance to the referring Party.

Assessing the amount due   3.2   The Parties are free to agree with the Adjudicator that he should decide apportionment of *fees* and Expenses. If they don't agree, the Parties pay equal shares. Adjudicators appointed under the Scheme decide the apportionment of *fees* and Expenses.

3.3   The Adjudicator will issue normal invoices after each decision has been made and notified to the Parties. In the event of a termination whilst an adjudication is in progress, an invoice is issued for the amount expended up to the date of termination.

3.4   The Adjudicator's *fee* is stated in the Contract Data. This will normally be in the form of an hourly rate. Time spent in travelling and preparation work is payable at the hourly rate.

No specific provision has been made for an appointment fee since the intention under NEC contracts is that he is paid only for resolving specific disputes. Under some forms of contract, the Parties may require the Adjudicator to do certain things before a dispute arises. For example they may require him to visit the site periodically or to read contract documents to familiarise himself with the contract details and the progress being made. If this is the case, details of the agreed arrangements should be incorporated into the Adjudicator's Contract and the fee payable should be clearly stated. None of the NEC contracts cater for these additional duties since the Adjudicator's obligations are limited to dealing with specific disputes as they arise.

Payment 3.7 The *interest rate* stated in the Contract Data should be based on an appropriate reliable annual base rate. The additional percentage is intended to reflect current commercial rates.

3.8 This subclause describes the joint and several liability of the Parties for payment of the Adjudicator's *fee* and Expenses. Although the Parties are required to pay the amount due to the Adjudicator in equal shares, he can recover the full amount from the other Party if one defaults. This avoids the need for the Adjudicator to take legal action against the defaulting Party, possibly disqualifying himself from further adjudication under the contract. As between the Parties, the one in default is required to reimburse the other any payments made to the Adjudicator on his behalf. If under subclause 1.8 there are more than two parties to a dispute, subclause 1.5 applies as to 'Party' in the singular or plural.

4 Termination

4.1 The Parties are able to terminate the Adjudicator's appointment, on condition that they both agree to do so. Termination is effected by both Parties notifying the Adjudicator of their agreement to terminate. In the absence of any express provision regarding payment, the payment clauses in Section 3 apply – the Parties pay the Adjudicator the amount due calculated in accordance with subclause 3.4.

4.2 This subclause states the circumstances which entitle the Adjudicator to terminate his appointment. If an advanced payment has been agreed but is not made, the Adjudicator is entitled to terminate immediately and is not obliged to continue with the adjudication.

4.3 In some circumstances, adjudicable disputes may arise over a considerable period of time. In order to avoid lengthy appointments, provision is made in this subclause for a termination date to be stated in the Contract Data. In normal circumstances, a date of one year after completion of the work or services is recommended. If an adjudicator is required after this termination date, the Adjudicator's Contract may be extended by agreement, or a new contract negotiated. If a different person is appointed as Adjudicator, a new Adjudicator's Contract will be required. Alternatively, the Parties may elect not to make an appointment at that stage on the basis that disputes are then unlikely to occur. Appointments of adjudicators for particular disputes as they arise will terminate when the decision is made and the Contract Data should make that clear. Thus the duration of appointment is not relevant.

Flow charts for the

Adjudicator's Contract

FLOW CHARTS

PREFACE

These flow charts depict the procedures followed when using the NEC3 Adjudicator's Contract (AC). They are intended to help people using the AC to see how the various AC clauses produce clear and precise sequences of action for the people involved.

The flow charts are not part of any contract. Much of the text and many of the words taken from the AC itself are abbreviated in the flow charts. The flow charts depict almost all of the sequences of action set out in the AC. Many of the sequences interact, and because of this, users of the flow charts will often have to review more than one sheet in order to track the full sequence of actions in one area.

PREFACE

ABBREVIATIONS USED IN THE FLOW CHART BOXES

FC 1.9   Flow chart for clause 1.9

CD   Contract Data

ABBREVIATIONS USED IN THE FLOW CHART BOXES

Legend

CHART START

HEADINGS
    Headings in caps
    provide guidance

STATEMENTS
    If a subclause is
    referenced, text
    is from the NEC

LOGIC LINKS
    Links go to right
    and/or downward
    unless shown

QUESTION
    Answer question
    to determine the
    route to follow

SUBROUTINE
    Include another
    flow chart here

CONTINUATION
    Link to matching
    point(s) on other
    chart sheets

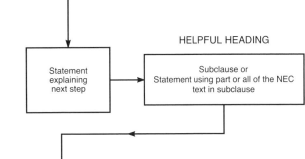

CHART TITLE
    Chart number,
    title and sheet

Flow chart or Sheet 1 of 2
Description

CONTINUATION

CHART FINISH

Flow chart or Sheet 2 of 2
Description

CHART TITLE

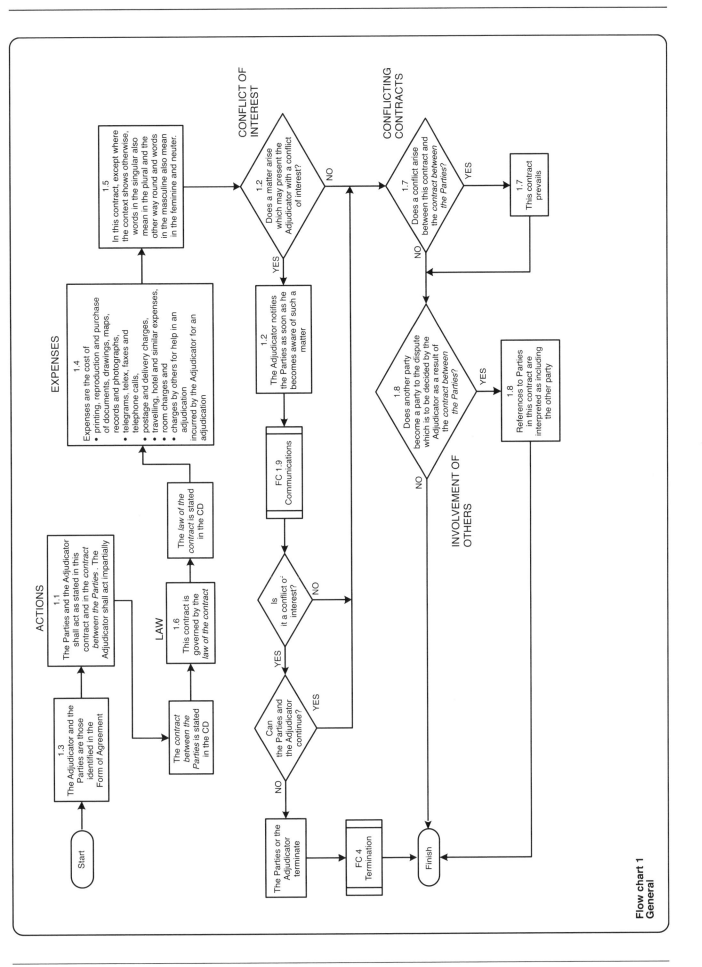

Flow chart 1
General

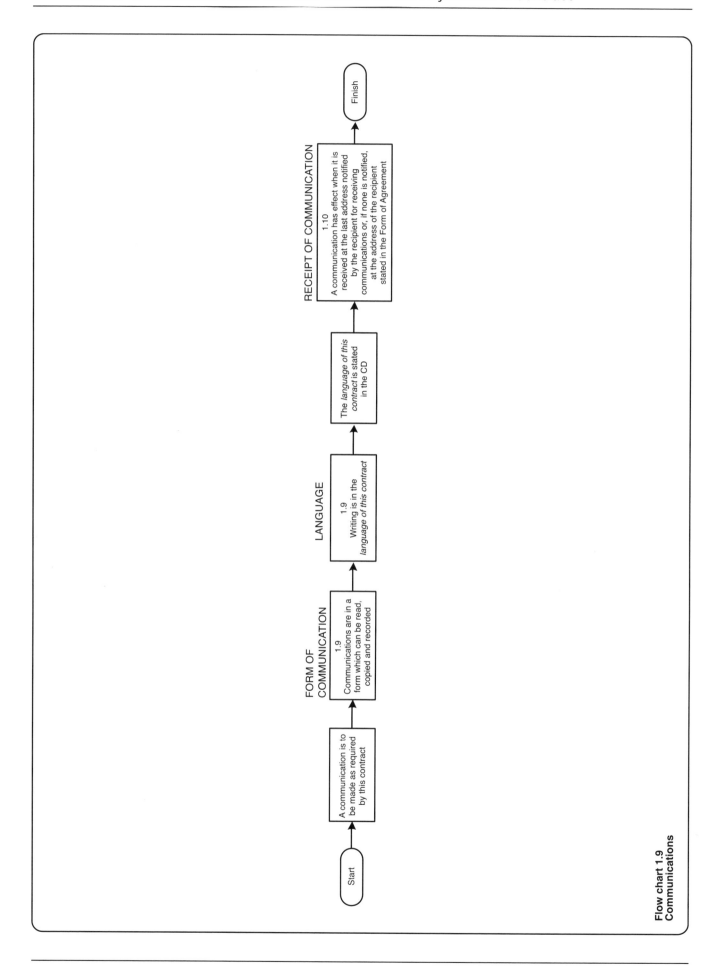

Start

A communication is to be made as required by this contract

FORM OF COMMUNICATION

1.9
Communications are in a form which can be read, copied and recorded

LANGUAGE

1.9
Writing is in the *language of this contract*

The *language of this contract* is stated in the CD

RECEIPT OF COMMUNICATION

1.10
A communication has effect when it is received at the last address notified by the recipient for receiving communications or, if none is notified, at the address of the recipient stated in the Form of Agreement

Finish

**Flow chart 1.9
Communications**

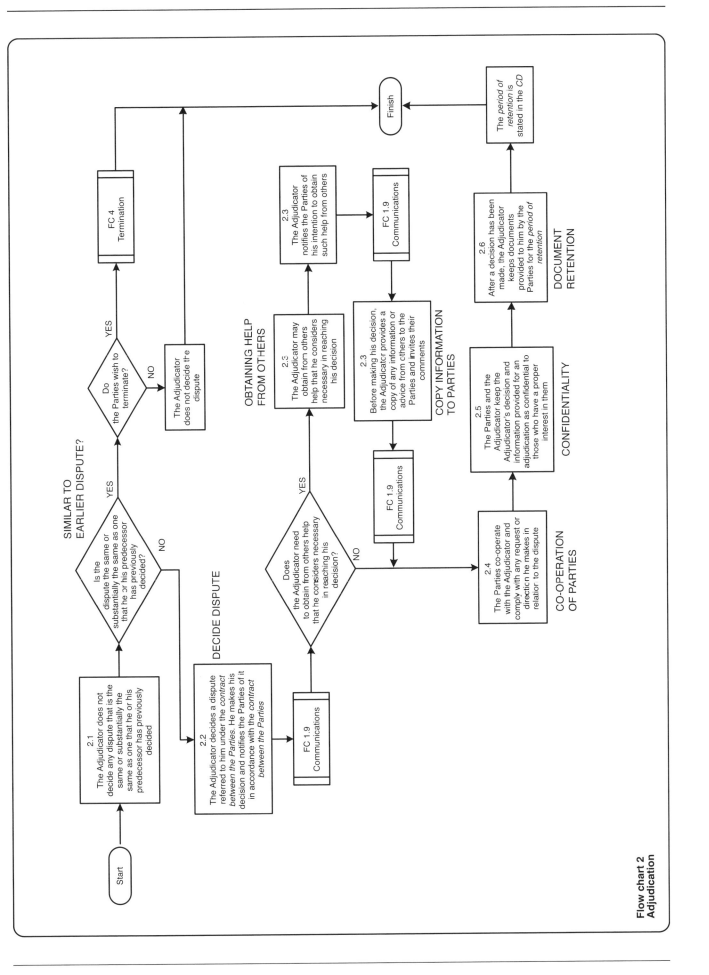

Flow chart 2
Adjudication

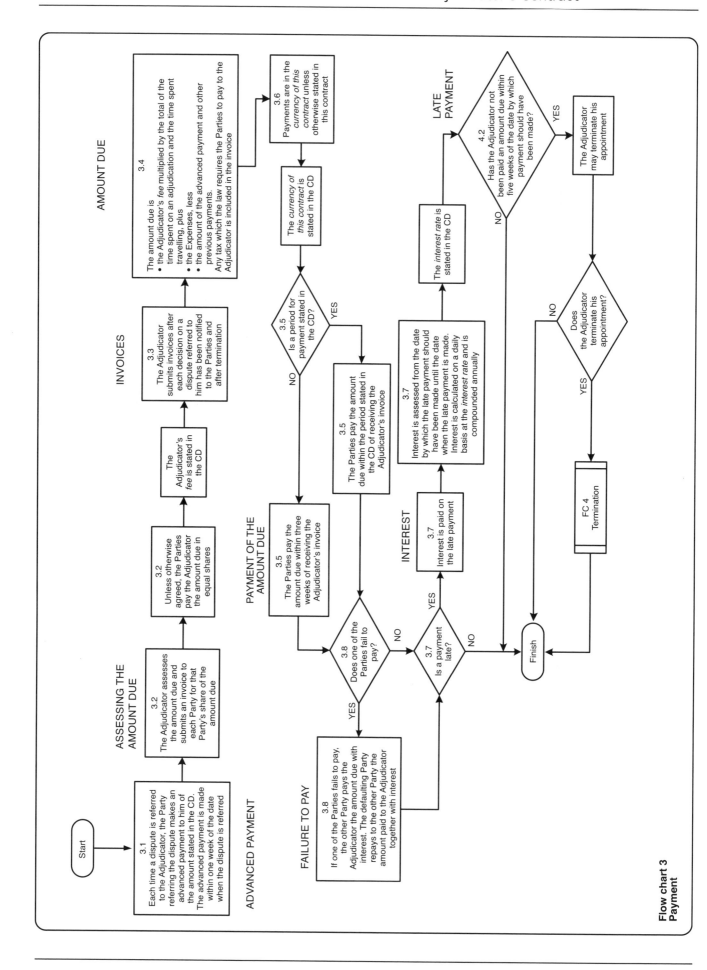

Flow chart 3
Payment

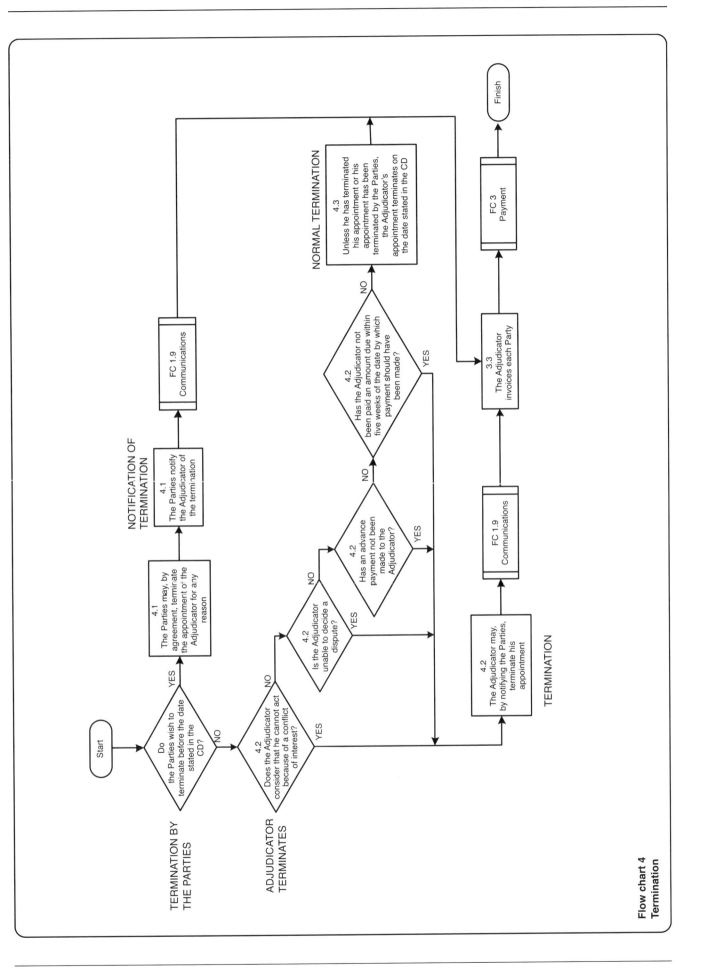

TERMINATION BY THE PARTIES

Start

Do the Parties wish to terminate before the date stated in the CD?

4.1
The Parties may, by agreement, terminate the appointment of the Adjudicator for any reason

YES

NOTIFICATION OF TERMINATION

4.1
The Parties notify the Adjudicator of the termination

FC 1.9
Communications

NO

ADJUDICATOR TERMINATES

4.2
Does the Adjudicator consider that he cannot act because of a conflict of interest?

NO

4.2
Is the Adjudicator unable to decide a dispute?

NO

4.2
Has an advance payment not been made to the Adjudicator?

NO

4.2
Has the Adjudicator not been paid an amount due within five weeks of the date by which payment should have been made?

NO

YES

YES

YES

NORMAL TERMINATION

4.3
Unless he has terminated his appointment or his appointment has been terminated by the Parties, the Adjudicator's appointment terminates on the date stated in the CD

Finish

YES

TERMINATION

4.2
The Adjudicator may, by notifying the Parties, terminate his appointment

FC 1.9
Communications

3.3
The Adjudicator invoices each Party

FC 3
Payment

Flow chart 4
Termination

APPENDIX 1

CONTRACT DATA – worked example

- The *contract between the Parties* is building and civil engineering work relating to the construction of new offices at 17 London Road, Rotherham, South Yorkshire.
- The *period of retention* is 4 weeks.
- The *law of the contract* is the law of England and Wales.
- The *language of this contract* is English.
- The amount of the advanced payment is £2,000.00.
- The Adjudicator's *fee* is £85.00 per hour.
- The *interest rate* is 5% per annum above the base lending rate of Barclays Bank plc.
- The *currency of this contract* is pounds sterling (£).
- The Adjudicator's appointment terminates on 31 December 2007.
- The period for payment of invoices is two weeks.

> If appointment is made for a single dispute, entry would be 'the issue of the adjudication decision'

    www.neccontract.com